THE OFFICIAL
LEGO® Harry Potter™
2023 Yearbook

Look at the picture in the middle of Harry, Ron and Hermione. Can you work out which of the four other pictures is its perfect mirror reflection?

A

C

B

D

Each Hogwarts house has its own crest. Look at the sequences of crests on the right, and try to find them within the grid. One has been found for you.

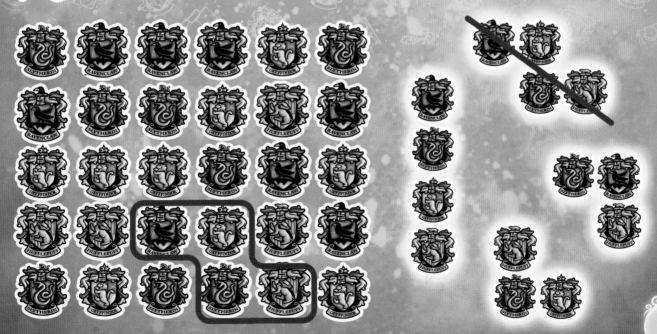

Students are assigned to their school houses during the Sorting Ceremony. Read the clues to work out which character leads the ceremony, and put a tick in their circle.

The Sorting Ceremony is led by:

· A person with headwear.
· A person wearing a long robe.
· A person who has a wand.

F

M

2

G

Neville has forgotten where he left his Remembrall, which he got from his grandmother. Can you find it in the pile of magical items?

Help Harry, Ron and Hermione get to Madam Hooch's flying lesson as quickly as possible.

In the circles below, Hogwarts teachers are placed opposite the classes they teach. Use the code to complete the circles with their missing symbols.

Potions

Charms

Flying

Transfiguration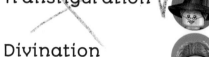

Divination

Astronomy

Which of the students on the right is a Quidditch player?
It's the one who is not watching from the crowd.

Harry received an unusual birthday present from Hagrid.
Colour the picture according to the code to find out what it is.

Look for ten differences between these two pictures of Harry and his friends trying out the magic pen.

Write the letters in the correct spaces to complete this picture of Hermione meeting Grawp, a giant who lives in the Forbidden Forest.

A

B

C

D

Draco doesn't go anywhere without his faithful companions. Divide the portraits into four groups, so that each group includes Malfoy, Crabbe and Goyle. One group has been done for you.

Professor Lockhart has released some Cornish pixies. Which of the four paths, when placed on the grid, will successfully capture all seven pixies?

Come on now. Round them up. Round them up. They're only pixies.

A

B

C

D

Hermione has drunk Polyjuice Potion containing cat hair! Connect the dots to see how she looks now.

Untangle the lines to find out which spell Professor Dumbledore used when Harry Potter fell off a broom during a Quidditch match.

BOMBARDA MAXIMA

CONFUNDO

ARRESTO MOMENTUM

Hermione has cast the *Wingardium Leviosa* spell. Find an identical feather to the one levitating above her.

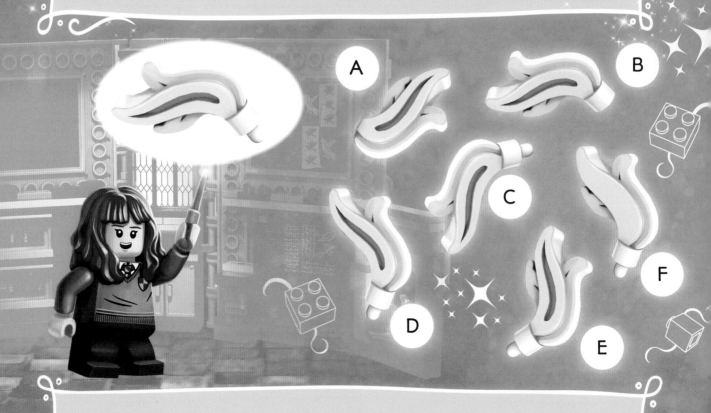

Restore the flying Ford Anglia to its former glory by writing the numbered fragments in the correct order.

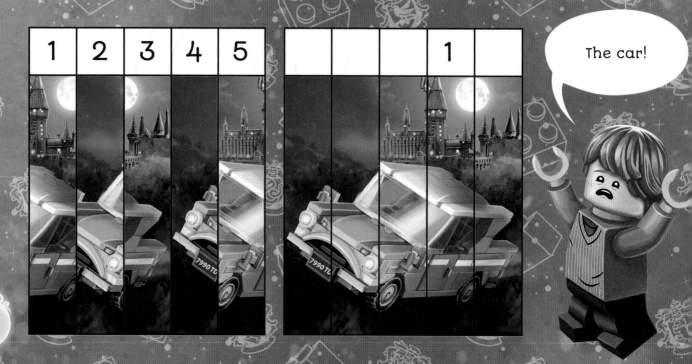

The car!

No one screams louder than Ron when spiders are around! Which coloured circle contains four different poses of Ron being scared?

Professor Lockhart loves admiring his appearance. Which of these mirrors shows his reflection?

Hagrid is not only a teacher, but also one of Harry's good friends. Use the steps below to draw your own picture of him.

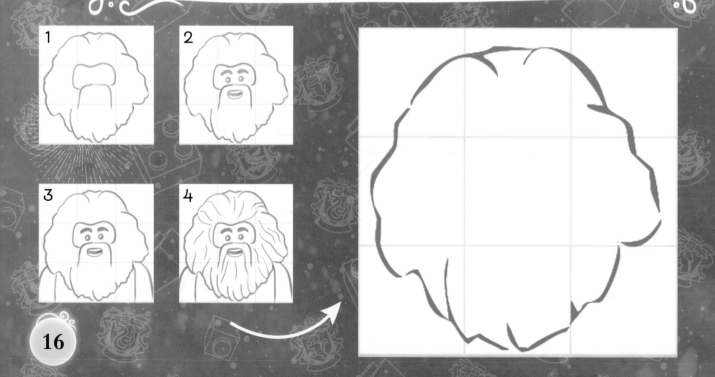

Draw lines to connect the matching pairs of Christmas trees. One has been drawn for you. The person who ends up with no line going through them was Hermione's date for the Yule Ball.

Find the matching owls in each neighbouring group. The third pair shows Errol, the Weasley family's owl.

Match the close-ups in the boxes to the teachers below. The teacher with no close-up is the one who wanted to escape from the Basilisk at Hogwarts.

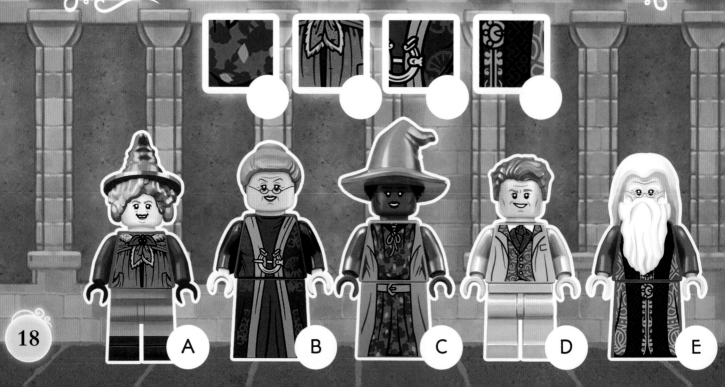

A   B   C   D   E

Honeydukes sweet shop is covered in snow! Clear the snow by writing the letters of the missing parts in the correct spaces. One has been done for you.

The Three Broomsticks is a famous inn. The inn is owned by the person who appears just once in the grid below.

The Patronus Charm takes the form of an animal, like Hermione's otter. What would your animal be? Draw it below.

Who has Ron lost a duel to? It's the character who is not obscured by any of the others.

I let her do that.

Ron and Hermione often argue, but they spend a lot of time together, too. Circle the jigsaw pieces that will bring them together.

22

Which line will lead Hagrid to Aragog,
his Acromantula friend?

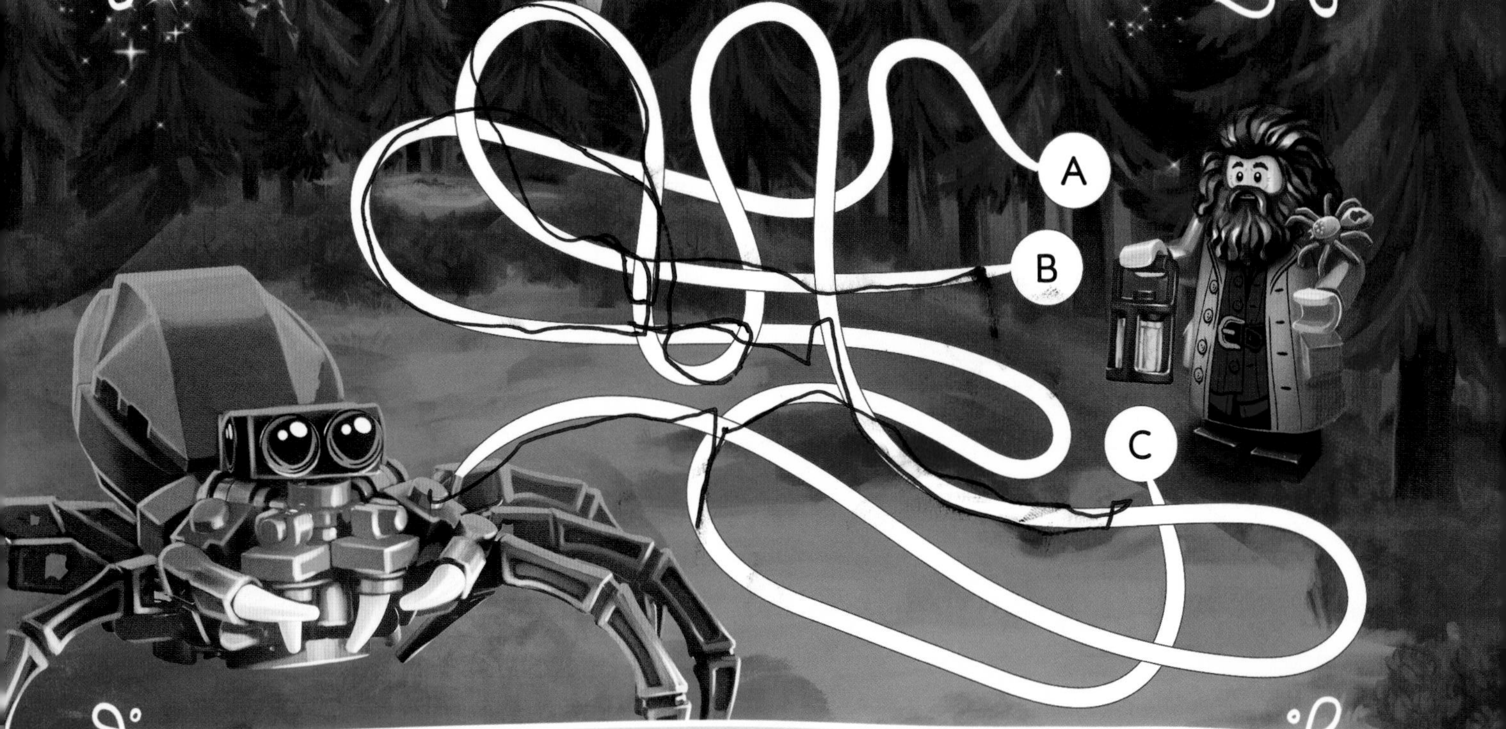

Find out who fainted when hearing a baby Mandrake's
scream by matching the outline to the character.

A

B

C

D

E

What precious thing is hidden inside the Sorting Hat?
Use the code to colour this picture and find out.

Help Ron find his way across this grid. He can't go diagonally, and he can only go on spaces where Hermione is smiling. His first few steps have been circled for you.

Welcome to the Slug Club Christmas party. Each of the smaller pictures contains one detail that is different from the main picture. Can you find each difference?

A

B

C

D

Magical feasts taste best with friends! Number the pictures from one to four, where one has the least food and four has the most.

Hermione loves studying books about magic. Fill in the blanks below so that each grid contains one blue book, one red book and two green books.

A

B

C

The Forbidden Forest hides many secrets. Count the creatures with green, blue and red eyes watching Ron and Hermione from the undergrowth.

Work your way along the frame below, copying the lines into the grid to create a path for Harry and Ron to follow all the way to Professor Slughorn's class. The first two have been done for you.

Complete this domino chain by adding the correct letters to the blank spaces. Where each domino connects to another, there should be two matching portraits. One has been done for you and characters can be used more than once.

A

B

C

D

E

Professor Slughorn has invited some students to a party at the Three Broomsticks. Can you find which character looks different in each picture?

You would be welcome, too.

Ginny has opened the Chamber of Secrets. Find the missing part of the door to close this secret room. The top of the door is the mirror image of the bottom.

A

B

C

D

Madam Pomfrey is caring for the unlucky characters who have been petrified by the Basilisk's gaze. Guide her to each character and through the exit without walking on any area of path more than once.

Professor Snape is looking for six combinations of potions.
Can you find each combination in the grid?

I can tell you how to bottle fame, brew glory and even put a stopper in death.

Ron must find a way through this game of Wizard's Chess. The sequences below tell him how many obstacles to avoid with each move. Which sequence is correct?

A ~~1~~-2-4-1-3-1-2-3-4
B ~~1~~-1-3-1-1-1-2-3-3
C ~~1~~-1-3-1-1-1-2-3-4

32

Herbology teacher, Professor Sprout, grows Mandrakes.
Find and circle all six magic seedlings in the picture.
One has been circled for you.

Harry and Professor Dumbledore are about to Apparate, which
takes them magically from one place to another. Follow the
symbols below to lead them to the Astronomy Tower.

These are the crests of the Durmstrang, Beauxbatons and Hogwarts schools. Each one has a mirror reflection containing one difference from the original image. Can you find the differences?

Ginny is a great Quidditch player. Complete her moves by following the sequence and adding in the missing letters.

A   B   C   D   E   F

Every witch is special and unique. Read each description and match it to a Hogwarts witch's picture.

1 Takes care of students when they are sick.
2 Conducts the Sorting Ceremony.
3 Knows everything about flying on a broom.
4 Plays Quidditch.
5 Grows magical plants.
6 Loves to read magical books.

Dobby is about to destroy Petunia Dursley's cake! Which cake is identical to the one Dobby is going to move?

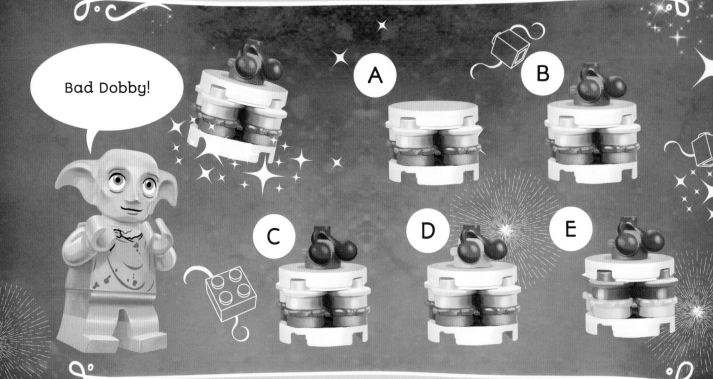

Bad Dobby!

A

B

C

D

E

The Cornish pixies have got Neville into trouble again!
Find the smaller squares within the big picture.
One has been found for you.

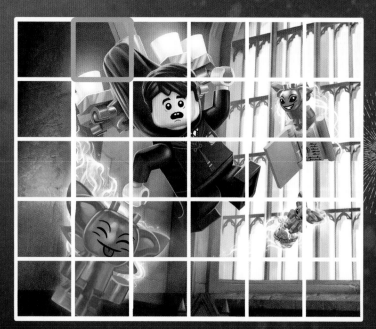

Harry and Draco are school rivals. Piece these ripped pictures back together by marking their circles in the same colour. One pair of pieces has been coloured for you.

Find the places where these former Hogwarts students appear next to each other. They can go side-to-side or up-and-down, but not diagonally.

Padfoot

Moony

Wormtail

Prongs

Only one of these items has a set of magic wands that matches the key. Find which one it is to discover what Ron likes to do in his spare time.

Harry and Draco are being cheered on at Duelling Club. All four characters at the bottom of the page appear somewhere in the scene. Put a tick in the circle next to each one when you find them.

Scared, Potter?

You wish.

Neville is on his way to a secret meeting with Dumbledore's Army. Find a path to the door, moving only in the direction of the arrows.

START

All student organizations are banned.

FINISH

Connect Luna, Harry and Ron with their Patronuses by untangling the paths.

Study this gallery of magical creatures for one minute, and then turn the page for a memory challenge.

The key is to concentrate.

Without looking back to the previous page, mark which creature appeared in each blank space on the grid.

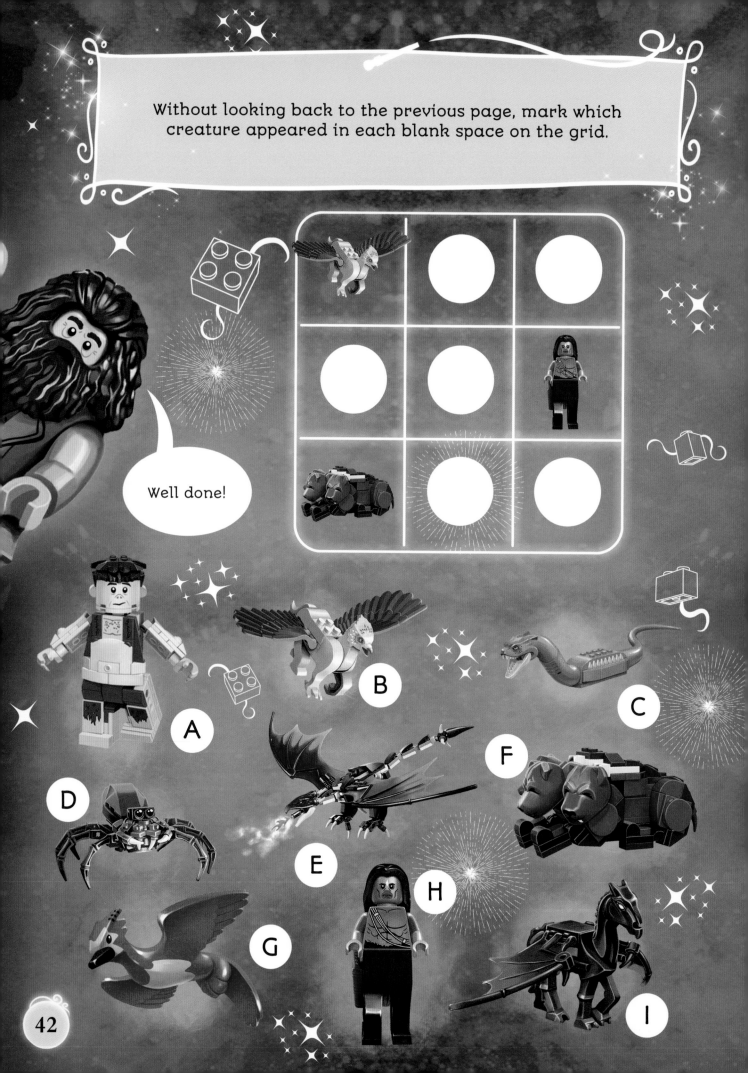

Well done!

Hufflepuff Quidditch team captain is trying to sort these Golden Snitches into matching pairs. Can you help him?

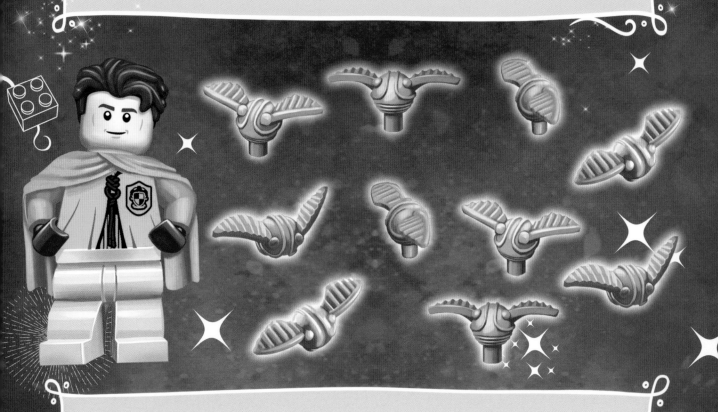

Count how many times each character appears in the below grid. The character who appears the most is the one who often gets Harry into trouble.

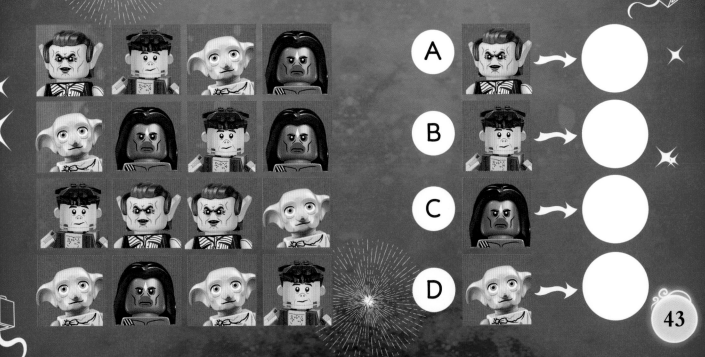

Luna often wears a lion hat to show her support for Gryffindor. However, she belongs in Ravenclaw. Use the code to colour in the squares and reveal the Ravenclaw crest.

Which witch or wizard's moonlit shadow
can you see in the Great Lake?

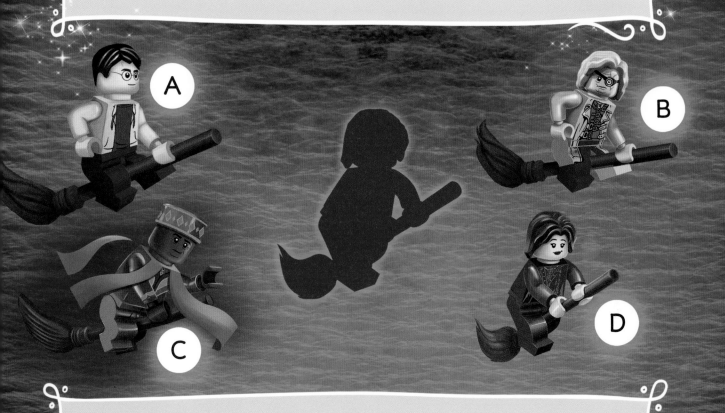

Six wizards drank Polyjuice Potion and turned into Harry. Find
the real Harry. He's the one who is different from the others.

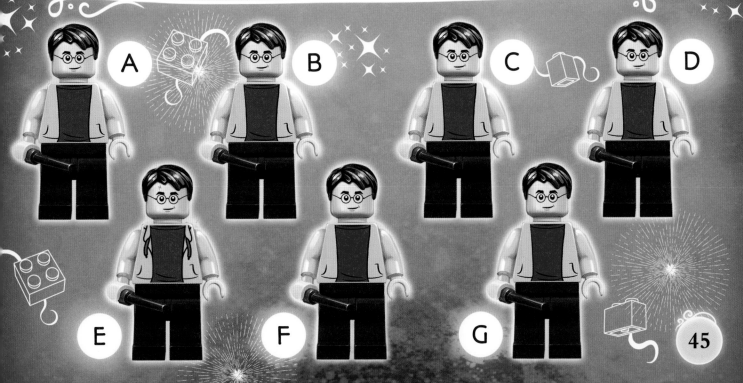

Match the description to the character to find out who Neville is most afraid of.

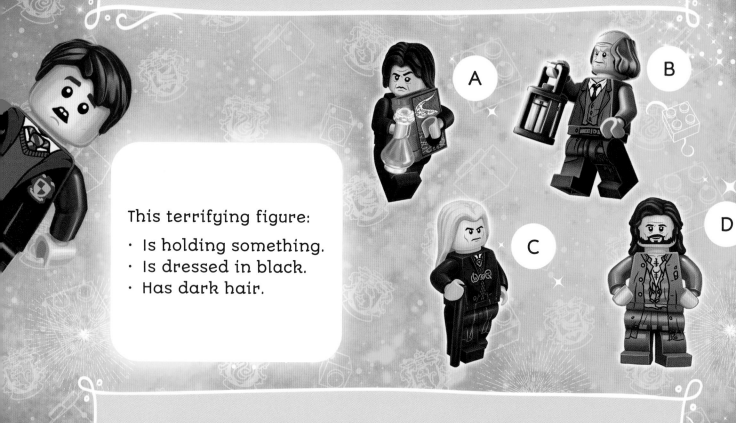

This terrifying figure:
· Is holding something.
· Is dressed in black.
· Has dark hair.

A

B

C

D

Count the vials on the paths. The path with the most potion vials will reveal the student who found a textbook belonging to the mysterious Half-Blood Prince.

Hermione is having a hard time with one of her school subjects. Make your way through the maze to find out which subject it is.

It's a woolly discipline.

Defence Against the Dark Arts

Potions

Divination

Nearly Headless Nick is one of the ghosts living in Hogwarts. Colour him in so that he looks transparent. His colours should match the colours behind him.

I prefer Sir Nicholas, if you don't mind!

Find the portrait below that has no matching pair to discover who planned Harry's escape from the Dursley's house.

Draw lines to pair up the matching potion vials.
The person who is not crossed by any of the lines is
the student who used Polyjuice Potion to turn into
Crabbe. One line has been drawn for you.

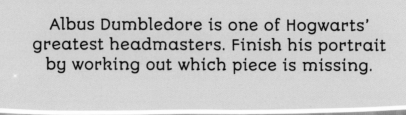

Albus Dumbledore is one of Hogwarts'
greatest headmasters. Finish his portrait
by working out which piece is missing.

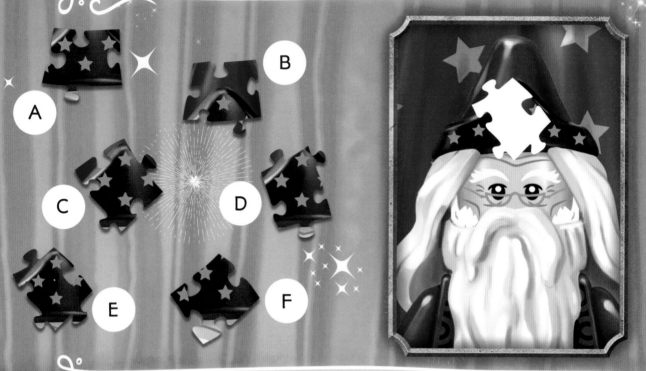

A

B

C

D

E

F

Find the path of arrows that matches the code, to see who
Death Eater Barty Crouch Jr is impersonating.

A

B

C

D

Fred and George are identical twin wizards, but there are ten differences between these two pictures. Can you find them all?

Harry had to face the Hungarian Horntail during the first task of the Triwizard Tournament. Look at the snapshots below and circle 'Y' if they appear in the scene and 'N' if they don't.

 Y N

 Y N

 Y N

 Y N

 Y N

 Y N

Which student brewed the perfect potion? It's the person who is not in the cloud of smoke.

A

B

C

D

Imagine you are a journalist on *The Daily Prophet*.
Draw what the front page would look like.

the
Daily Prophet

Match the close-ups to the Gryffindor Quidditch players. The player who is not in any of the close-ups is in charge of the team.

A

B

C

D

E

F

Each Quidditch team has its own colour. Colour the crests in the correct order to complete the pathway to the finish.

Gryffindor   Hufflepuff   Ravenclaw   Slytherin

START

FINISH

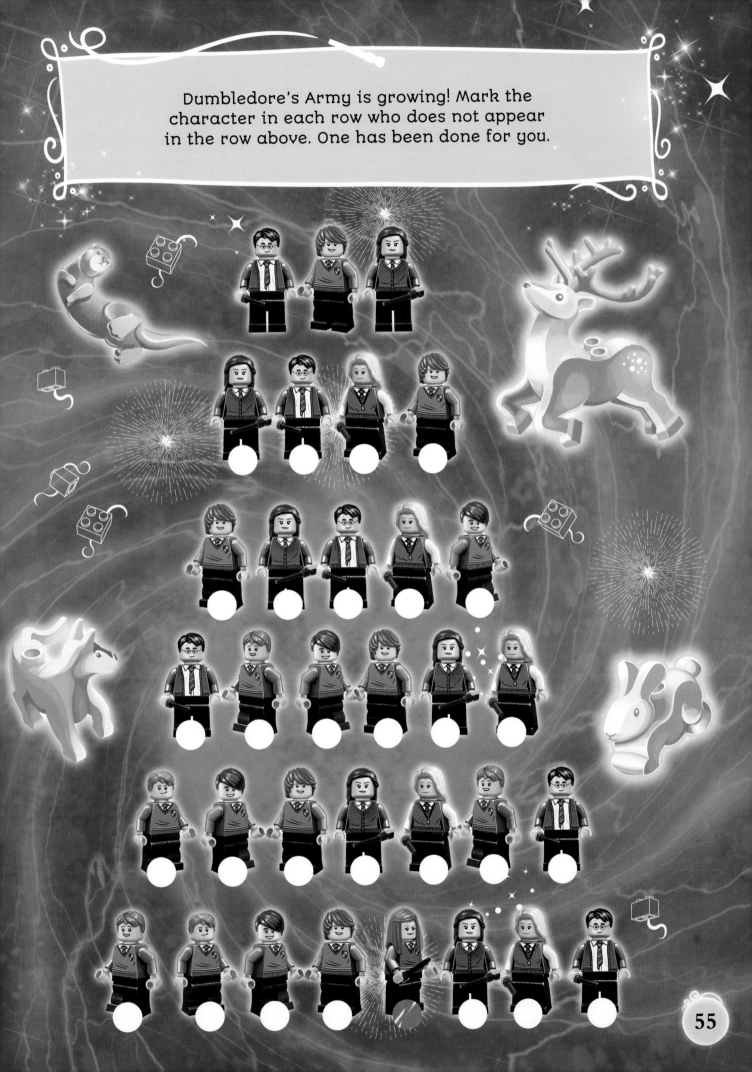

Dumbledore's Army is growing! Mark the character in each row who does not appear in the row above. One has been done for you.

Look at the sequences on the left and draw around them in the grid. The character who is left at the end is the person who was saved by Harry after accidentally drinking a strong love potion.

Number the vials in order from largest to smallest, to see the order Hermione will combine them in for her next potion. One has been done for you.

1

Ginny is helping Harry hide the Half–Blood Prince's textbook. Follow the colour code on the left to find what hiding place they are going to choose.

ANSWERS

P. 4

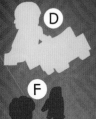

P. 5

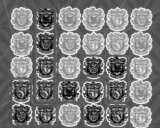

P. 6

P. 7

P. 8

P. 9

P. 10

P. 11

P. 12

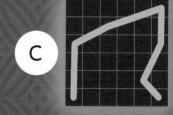

P. 13

P. 14

ARRESTO MOMENTUM

P. 15

P. 16

P. 17

P. 18

P. 19

E H
B
D
F A
G C

C A
B E

P. 20

P. 21

P. 22

C

B

P. 23

C

P. 24

P. 25

A B

C D

P. 26

4 3

2 1

P. 27

⊙⊙ = 5

⊙⊙ = 7

⊙⊙ = 6

P. 29

P. 28

A B

C

C

B

D A

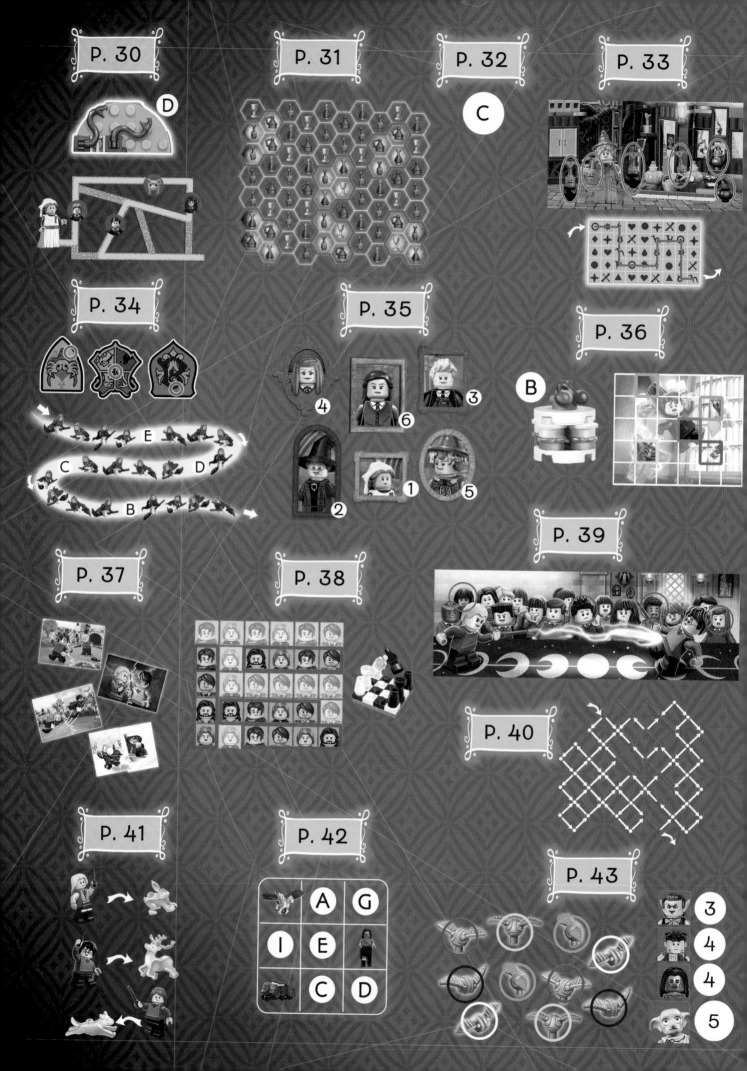

D

E

C

D

B

4

2

6

1

3

5

A   G

I   E

C   D

3

4

4

5

D

E

A

E

C

E

C

F D C A B

C

How to build Hermione